ILLUSTRATED CLASSICS
BLACK BEAUTY

by Anna Sewell
Abridged by Elaine Ife
Illustrated by Libby Turner

BRIMAX BOOKS · NEWMARKET · ENGLAND

INTRODUCTION

Black Beauty was written by Anna Sewell in the last years of her life, when she was crippled and often very weak and ill. Anna was born in Norfolk in 1820; her mother was a shy nervous person who had tried her hand at writing, but with only modest success. Her father was a failed business man who nevertheless worked long hours to earn enough money to support his family.

After two accidents Anna's health began to fail and by the age of forty she was lame in both feet, and had to travel everywhere outside her home in a pony carriage. Her aim in writing *Black Beauty* was to make people more aware of the suffering and harsh treatment to which horses were subjected at that time; and this theme is constant throughout the story. It is written from the horse's viewpoint and tells the story of a handsome well-bred horse from his very first days as a young colt, through his early years at Birtwick Park and on to harder times as a London cab-horse. Black Beauty befriends at Birtwick Park a mare called Ginger whose story is far from happy and whose treatment at the hands of her masters clearly demonstrates Miss Sewell's motives in writing her book.

The social classes which existed in England in the late nineteenth century are very clearly defined, but it is plain that goodness of character is a matter of personal choice rather than social status, for who could be kinder or more considerate than Jerry Barker the cab-driver, and who more unfeeling and cruel than "her ladyship" at Earlshall Park?

Black Beauty was advised by his mother always to "do your work with a good will, lift your feet up well when you trot, and never bite or kick even in play," and he heeds this advice whatever befalls him. The unlucky Ginger cannot find the spirit to keep an even temper after all she has endured, for she says, "It's no use, men are strongest, and if they are cruel and have no feeling, there is nothing that we can do, but just bear it, bear it on and on to the end."

Anna Sewell did not live to see her book achieve its great success. Millions of copies have been sold throughout the world, and the story of Black Beauty has become one of the classics of our time.

CONTENTS

© BRIMAX RIGHTS LTD 1985. All rights reserved
First published in Great Britain by
BRIMAX BOOKS, Newmarket, England 1985
ISBN 0 86112 264 X
Printed in Belgium

My Early Home

The first place that I can remember clearly was a large pleasant meadow, with a pond of clear water and some shady trees. As we looked over the hedge to one side we saw a field and on the other side by the road, was our master's house. At the top of the meadow was a plantation of fir trees, while a brook flowed along the far end.

I was too young to eat grass at first and lived on my mother's milk. In the day-time I ran by her side and at night I lay down close by her. In hot weather we stood in the shade of the trees and when it was cold we had a warm shed near the plantation. When I was older my mother went out to work each day but returned in the evening.

There were six young colts in the meadow with me, some of whom were older and bigger than I was, but we were all friends and played happily together. My mother did not like their rough ways, and one day she spoke to me:

"These colts are very good but they have not learned any manners. You have been well bred and well born and I hope you will grow up to be gentle and good. Do your work willingly. Lift your feet up well when you trot, and never bite or lick even in play."

I have never forgotten my mother's advice for she was a wise old horse. Her name was Duchess, but our master called her Pet.

10

We were all very fond of our master for he was a good man and treated us well. He nicknamed me Darkie, as my coat was a dull black. Sometimes he gave me a piece of bread and brought a carrot for my mother.

Our master paid a boy to do the rough work. Dick was the boy's name. As he walked along by the hedge eating berries he would throw sticks and stones at us. Usually they missed but not always. One day, the master caught him at this game and boxed his ears, shouting,

"You bad boy to chase the colts. I was just waiting to see you with my own eyes. Take your money and don't ever set foot on my farm again." Old Daniel, whose job was to care for the horses, was a gentle fellow, so we had a good life.

11

The Hunt

Before I was two years old something happened which I shall never forget. It was a cold and misty spring morning and we were feeding at the end of the field when we heard in the distance the cry of dogs.

"There are the hounds," said one of the colts, and cantered off up the field. The rest of us followed to see what was happening.

"They have found a hare," said my mother. "If they come this way we shall see the hunt."

The noise of those hounds came nearer and filled the air, "Yo! Yo o o! yo oo!"

After them came a number of men on horseback, some of them in green coats, all galloping as fast as they could. They came to a standstill in a nearby field; the dogs stopped barking and ran about with their noses to the ground. "They have lost the scent," said the older horse, "perhaps the hare will escape."

"What hare?" I said.

"Oh, any hare they find will do for the dogs and men to run after." Just then the dogs came back all together at full speed. "Now we shall see the hare," said my mother. As she spoke, a hare, wild with fright, rushed by, and close behind came the dogs. They burst over the bank, leapt the stream and came dashing across the field, followed by the huntsmen. The hare tried to get through the fence, but it was too thick and she turned sharply round to make for the road, but it was too late; the dogs were upon her with their wild cries; we heard one shriek, and that was the end of her.

I was so astonished by this cruel scene that I did not notice what was going on by the brook. Two fine horses were down, one was struggling in the stream, and the other was groaning in the grass. One of the riders was getting out of the water covered with mud, the other lay quite still.

"The man's neck is broken," said my mother. "I am sad to see it, but in all my days I can never understand why men are so fond of this sport; so often they are injured or their horses badly hurt, and all for a hare or a fox or a stag, which they could easily get some other way. But there, we are only horses, and don't know."

Whilst my mother was speaking we stood and looked on. My master was first to raise the injured man. He seemed in a very bad way and everyone looked serious. They carried him to the master's house, and someone rode off to tell Squire Gordon of the accident, for the injured man was his son. The farmer, Mr Bond, was sent for, and he examined the black horse. He shook his head and said one of his legs was broken. A gun was brought and presently we heard a loud bang and the black horse moved no more. My mother told us that his name was Rob Roy. She had known him for many years and said he was a good and brave horse.

Some days later we heard the church bell tolling for a long time and saw several black coaches drawn by black horses. They were carrying young Gordon to the churchyard to bury him. He would never ride again. I did not understand what had happened to Rob Roy but I knew that it all took place because of one little hare.

My Breaking In

I was now beginning to grow handsome; my coat had grown fine and soft, and was a shiny black. I had one white foot and a pretty white star on my forehead. When I was four years old Squire Gordon came to look at me. He examined my eyes, my mouth and my legs, felt them all down; and then I had to walk and trot and gallop before him. He said he would take me when I had been broken in. Not everyone will know what breaking in is, so I will tell you. It means to teach a horse to wear a saddle and bridle, and to carry on his back a man, woman, or child; to go just the way they wish, and to go quietly. I had been used to a halter and a headstall, and to being led about in the fields and lanes quietly, but now I was to have a bit and bridle. My master gave me some oats and spoke kindly to me, as he put the bit into my mouth, and the bridle fixed, but it was a nasty thing! It was made of cold hard steel, as thick as a man's finger. It was pushed into my mouth, and held tightly by straps, so that it would not move. Next came the saddle, but that was not nearly as bad. My master was very kind to me and always brought me a few oats to encourage me. Finally, when he thought I was ready, he got on my back and rode me round the meadow on the soft grass.

Some time later I was taken to the blacksmith to have iron shoes fitted. I felt no pain, though my feet felt very stiff and heavy, but there were more new things to wear! First a heavy collar on my neck and a bridle with great side-pieces called blinkers. Next there was a small saddle with a nasty hard strap that went right under my tail; that was the crupper, and I hated that as much as the bit. I felt as though I wanted to kick out in protest but, of course, I could not kick such a good master, so in time I got used to everything and could do my work as well as my mother.

It was early in May when a man came from Squire Gordon's and took me away to the Hall. My master said, "Goodbye, Darkie. Be a good horse and always do your best."

I could not say goodbye, so I put my nose into his hand. He patted me kindly, and I left my first home.

Birtwick Park

Squire Gordon's Park was on the outskirts of the village of Birtwick. It was a fairly large property at the centre of which stood a fine house and gardens. Beyond these lay the home paddock, the old orchard and the stables. The groom led me into a large square stall. It was clean, sweet and airy and the sides were low enough to let me see around. He gave me some very nice oats, he patted me, spoke kindly and then went away.

In the stall next to mine stood a little fat grey pony, with a thick mane and tail, a very pretty head and a pert little nose. "How do you do," I said. "What is your name?"

He turned, held up his head and replied, "My name is Merrylegs. I am well liked and trusted here. Are you going to live next door to me in the box?"

I said, "Yes."

"Well then," he said, "I hope you are good-tempered. I do not like anyone next door who bites." Just then a horse's head looked over from the stall beyond. The ears were laid back and the eye looked rather ill-tempered. She seemed very cross that I was in that particular stall. In the afternoon when she went out Merrylegs told me all about it.

"Ginger has a bad habit of biting and snapping," said Merrylegs. "That is why they call her Ginger; when she was in the loose box where you are standing, she used to snap very much, so they moved her. It is a bad habit she has; she says no one was ever kind to her before, so why should she not bite. I could understand it if she were treated badly here, but there is not a better place for a horse in the whole country than this. John is the best groom that ever was and James, the stable boy, treats all the horses well. It really is Ginger's own fault that she was moved out of that box."

The next morning I was led out into the yard and groomed carefully by John Manly, the coachman. The

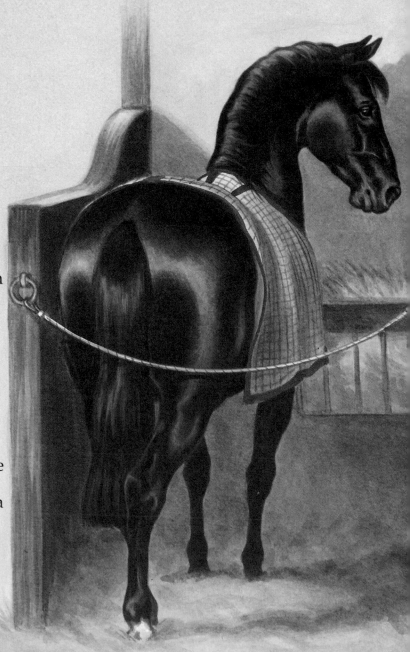

Squire came to look at me and seemed pleased. He told John to take me out and to see how I rode. As we came back through the Park we met the Squire and Mrs Gordon, and they asked John if I had done well.

"First rate, sir," answered John. "He is as swift as a deer and has a fine spirit too."

"That's good," said the Squire, "I will try him myself tomorrow."

I found the master to be a very good rider and thoughtful for his horse. Mrs Gordon was at the Hall as he rode up and the Squire spoke.

"He is exactly as John said, a good, sweet-tempered horse. What shall we call him?"

"Would you like Ebony?" she said. "He is as black as ebony."

"No, not Ebony."

"Will you call him Blackbird, like your uncle's old horse?"

"No, he is far handsomer than old Blackbird ever was."

"Yes," she said, "he is really quite a beauty. He has such a sweet, good-tempered face, and such a fine intelligent eye. What do you say to calling him Black Beauty?"

"Black Beauty – why yes, I think that is a very good name. If you like it, it shall be his name."

And so it was.

Ginger

One day when Ginger and I were standing alone in the shade we talked a great deal. She wanted to know all about my upbringing and breaking in, so I told her.

"Well," she said, "if I had your upbringing I might have been as good-tempered as you, but now I don't believe I ever shall."

"Why not?" I asked.

"Because it has all been so different for me," she replied. "I have never had anyone, horse or man, that was kind to me, or that I cared to please. There was no kind master like yours to look after me, talk to me, or bring me nice things to eat. When it came to breaking in, it was a bad time for me. Several men came and chased me into one corner of a field and forced open my mouth to push in the bit. They got the halter on by force, though I gave them plenty of trouble.

The master's son, Samson they called him, was a strong tall man, and boasted that he had never found a horse that could throw him. He had a hard voice, a hard eye and a hard hand; I felt from the first that what he wanted was to break my spirit and just make me into a quiet, humble, obedient piece of horse-flesh. One morning he came for me with a saddle and bridle and a new kind of bit. Something I did angered him and he tugged hard on the rein. The new bit was very painful and I reared up suddenly, which angered him more, and he began to flog me.

I felt my whole spirit set against him and I began to kick and plunge, and rear, as I had never done before. For a long time he stuck to the saddle and punished me cruelly with his whip and spurs, but I wanted only to get him off my back. At last, after a terrible struggle I threw him off backwards, and galloped off to the other end of the field. He slowly got up and went into the stable, but no one came to catch me. It was a hot afternoon and I was sore and hungry. At last, just as the sun went down my old master came out with food in his hand. He spoke kindly and cheerfully to me, 'Come along lassie, come along lassie, come along, come along.'

I ate some oats, and then quietly he led me to the stable. Samson stood at the door.

'Stand back,' said the master, 'and keep out of her way. You've done a bad day's work for this filly. A bad-tempered man will never make a good-tempered horse. You've not learned your trade yet, Samson.'

Then he led me into my box, took off the saddle and bridle, and sponged my sides gently with warm water. He looked at my mouth and saw how the skin was broken, so he told the man to fetch a good bran mash with some meal added to it.

After that he often came to see me, and when my mouth was healed, the other breaker, Job they called him, went on training me. He was steady and thoughtful and I soon learned what he wanted.

19

After my breaking in I was bought by a dealer to match another chestnut horse. For some weeks he drove us together and then we were sold to a fashionable gentleman and sent up to London. I had been driven with a bearing rein by the dealer and I hated it worse than anything else, but in this place we were reined far tighter. You have never had a bearing rein so you don't know what it is, but I can tell you it is dreadful. I was made to hold up my head for hours on end, unable to move it at all. It was enough to drive any horse mad. I grew more and more restless and irritable and one day the groom beat me. I could stand no more. I kicked and plunged with all my might and freed myself. Of course that was the end of that place. I was sent to an auction to be sold and another dealer took me. He realized that all I needed was a kind hand and finally I was brought here, not long before you arrived."

I was sorry for Ginger after all she had suffered, but I noticed that as the weeks went on she grew much more gentle and cheerful. One day James said,

"I do believe that mare is getting fond of me."

John said, "Yes, she'll soon be as good as Black Beauty. Kindness is all she wants, poor thing."

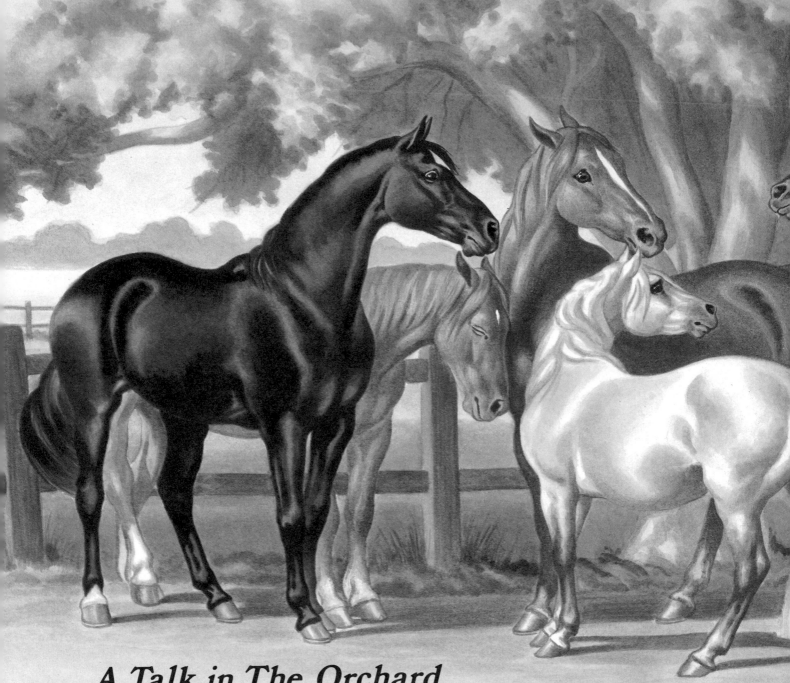

A Talk in The Orchard

Ginger and I were not of the regular tall carriage horse breed, we had more of the racing blood in us. We stood about fifteen and a half hands high, we were therefore just as good for riding as we were for driving, and our master used to say that he disliked either man or horse that could do only one thing; as he did not want to show off in London parks, he preferred a more active and useful kind of horse. As for us, our greatest pleasure was when we were saddled for a riding party; the master on Ginger, the mistress on me, and the young ladies of the household on Sir Oliver and Merrylegs. Sir Oliver was an old brown hunter, past work now, but a great favourite with the master. I had often wondered why he had such a very short tail, it was only six or seven inches long, with a tassel of hair hanging from it. One day in the orchard, I asked him what sort of accident had caused him to lose his tail.

"For fashion," said the old horse, with a stamp of his foot. "There was not a well-bred young horse in my time that did not have his tail docked in that shameful way, just as if the good God that made us did not know what we wanted and what looked best."

Sir Oliver, though he was gentle, was a fiery old fellow and what he said was all so new to me and so dreadful that I found a bitter feeling towards men, rise up in my mind. Ginger became excited and the discussion would have gone on but Merrylegs reminded us of our good fortune in being at Birtwick, under the care of kind men, such as James and John. To change the conversation I asked,

"Can any one tell me the use of blinkers?" Justine, a roan cob, answered me:

"They are supposed to prevent horses from shying and starting and getting so frightened as to cause accidents."

"I consider," said Sir Oliver, "that blinkers are dangerous things. We horses can see much better in the dark than man can, and many an accident would never have happened if horses had full use of their eyes."

Again Merrylegs broke in with a comment, "I'll tell you a secret. I believe that John does not approve of blinkers. I heard him talking with the master about it one day. He said it would be a good thing if all colts were broken in without blinkers, as was the case in some foreign countries; so let us cheer up and have a run to the other end of the orchard. I believe the wind has blown off some apples, so we might just as well eat them as the slugs."

"Accident!" he snorted, with a fierce look. "It was no accident! It was a cruel, shameful, cold-blooded act! When I was young I was taken to a place where these cruel things are done. I was tied up so that I could not move, and then they came and cut off my long beautiful tail, through the flesh and through the bone."

"How dreadful!" I exclaimed.

"What did they do it for?" asked Ginger.

A Stormy Day

One day late in autumn, my master had a long journey to make on business. I was put into the dog-cart, and John went with his master. There had been a great deal of rain and the wind was very high, blowing the dry leaves across the road in a shower. We went along merrily until we came to the toll-bar and the low wooden bridge. The river banks were rather high, and the bridge instead of rising, went across just level, so that in the middle, if the river was full, the water would be nearly up to the woodwork. The man at the gate said the river was rising fast and he feared it would be a bad night. Many of the fields were under water and in one low part of the road the water was halfway up to my knees; the ground was good and the master drove gently so it didn't matter.

The master's business in town kept him a long time and we did not start for home until late in the afternoon. The wind was much higher and I heard the master say to John that he had never been out in such a storm; I thought the same myself as we passed through a wood where the great branches were swaying and the rushing sound was terrible.

All of a sudden there was a groan and a crack and a splitting sound. A great oak, torn up by the roots, fell across the road in front of us. I was frightened but I did not move.

"That was close," said my master. "What shall we do now?"

"Well, sir," replied John, "we can't drive over the tree or round it.

All we can do is to go back to the crossroads and go the other way, but it will make us very late."

There was no alternative, so back we went. By the time we reached the bridge it was nearly dark. We were going along at a good pace, but the moment my feet touched the bridge I felt sure there was something wrong. I dared not go forward and I stopped straightaway.

"Go on Beauty," said my master, and he gave me a touch with the whip, but I dared not stir; he gave me a sharp cut, I jumped, but I dared not go forward.

"There's something wrong, sir," said John, and he sprang out of the dog-cart and came to my head and looked all around. He tried to lead me forward. "Come on Beauty, what's the matter?" Of course I could not tell him, but I knew very well that the bridge was not safe. Just then the man at the toll-gate on the other side ran out of the house, waving a torch.

"Hey! Hey! Hey! Stop there!" he cried. "What's the matter?" shouted my master.

"The bridge is broken in the middle and part of it has been carried away; if you move on any further you'll be in the river."

"Thank God!" said my master.

"You Beauty!" said John. He took the bridle and gently turned me round to the right hand road by the river side. It grew darker and darker, stiller and stiller. I trotted quietly along, the wheels hardly making a sound on the soft road.

At last we came to the Park gates. We saw a light at the hall door, and at the upper windows, and as we drew up, the mistress ran out saying,

"Are you really safe, my dear? Oh! I have been so anxious, imagining all sorts of things. Have you had an accident?"

"No, my dear, but if your Black Beauty had not been so wise, we should all have been carried down the river at the wooden bridge."

I heard no more as they went into the house and John took me to the stable. Oh! what a good supper he gave me that night, a good bran mash, and some crushed beans with my oats, and such a thick bed of straw. I was glad of it, for I was very tired.

James Howard

One morning, early in December, John had just led me into my box after my daily exercise, and James was coming in from the corn chamber with some oats, when the master came into the stable. He looked rather serious and held a letter in his hand. John fastened the door of my box, touched his cap and waited for orders.

"Good morning, John," said the master. "I want to know if you have any complaints to make about James?"

"Complaints, sir? No, sir."

"Does he work hard, and is he polite to you?"

"Yes, sir, always."

"You never find he gets lazy when your back is turned?"

"Never, sir. I can truthfully say that I never met a pleasanter or more honest young man. I trust what he says, and I know he does a good day's work. He is gentle and clever with the horses too, which is more than can be said of most stable boys I've met."

The master smiled.

"I am glad to hear you say so, for that is exactly the opinion I have formed of the boy."

James had been standing at the door all this time, and now the master asked him to come closer.

"James, my boy, put down the oats and come here. I shall tell you now why I was making all these inquiries. I have a letter here from my brother-in-law, Sir Clifford Williams of Clifford Hall. He wants me to find him a trustworthy groom of about twenty or twenty-one, who knows his job. I don't want to part with you but it would be a good start for you.

"How old are you now, James?"

"Nineteen next May, sir."

"That's young. What do you think John?"

"Well sir, he is young, but he is big and strong. He hasn't had much experience in driving but he has a firm hand and a quick eye."

"Very well then, James. Think it over. Talk to your mother at dinner time, and let me know your decision."

It was agreed after a few days that James should go to Clifford Hall in a month or six weeks, and in the meantime he was to have as much practice in driving as possible.

27

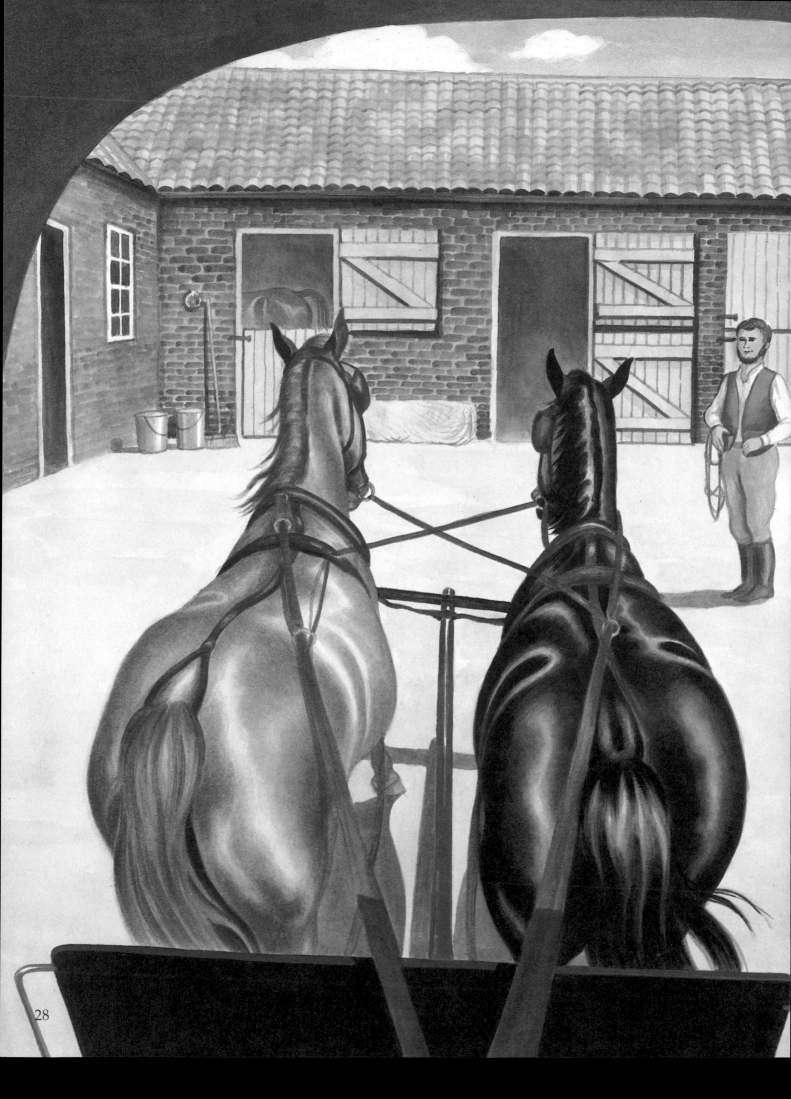

The Old Ostler

I never knew the carriage go out so often before. John rode with James at first, to give him advice and after that James drove alone. Soon after this, the master and mistress decided to visit some friends who lived about forty-six miles away, and James was to drive them. He drove very carefully and helped us a good deal. The first night we stopped at a large hotel in the Market Place of the town. We drove under an archway into a long yard at the end of which were the stables and coach-houses. Two ostlers came to take us out. The head ostler was a pleasant active little man, with a crooked leg and a yellow striped waistcoat. He took off my harness and led me to a long stable, while the other man brought Ginger.

I was never cleaned so lightly and quickly as by that little old man. James, who had been watching, could hardly believe his eyes.

"Well," he said, "I thought I was pretty quick and our John quicker still, but you beat us both for being quick and thorough at the same time."

"Practice makes perfect," said the crooked little ostler. "Bless you! It's only a matter of habit. If you get into the habit of being quick, it's just as easy as being slow. I've worked with horses since I was twelve years old in hunting stables and racing stables. I couldn't live without them. I can tell you, it's a downright pleasure to handle a horse like this one, well-bred, well-mannered and well cared for."

"That's the way our master treats the horses," said James.

"Who is your master young man, if you don't mind my asking?"

"He is Squire Gordon of Birtwick Park, the other side of the Beacon hills," said James.

"Ah yes. I have heard of him, a wonderful judge of horses I believe and one of the best riders in the country."

While this conversation was going on, the other man had finished cleaning Ginger and brought our corn, and James and the old man left the stable together.

The Fire

I slept for some hours that night but woke up suddenly feeling very uncomfortable. The air seemed all thick and choking. I heard Ginger coughing and one of the other horses moving about restlessly. It was quite dark and I could see nothing but the stable was very full of smoke, and I hardly knew how to breathe. I heard steps outside, and one of the ostlers burst into the stable with a lantern, and began to untie the horses, and try to lead them out. He seemed in such a hurry and so frightened that he frightened me still more. The first horse would not go with him, nor the second or third. He tried to drag me out by force, but it was no use. He tried us all in turn and then left the stable.

I looked upward and saw a red light flickering on the wall. Someone outside cried, "Fire!" The old ostler came in quickly and quietly and led one horse out, but the flames were growing higher every second.

The next thing I heard was James's voice, quiet and cheery as it always was.

"Come my beauties, it is time for us to be off, so wake up and come along."

He slipped my bridle on and covered my eyes and shouted,

"Here somebody, take this horse while I go back for the other."

There was much confusion in the yard with horses being led out of other stables and people shouting all sorts of things. Presently I heard above all the noise a loud clear voice, which I knew was the master's:

"James Howard! James Howard! Are you there?"

There was no answer, but I heard a crash of something falling in the stable and the next moment I gave a loud joyful neigh, for I saw James coming through the smoke leading Ginger with him.

"My brave lad," said the master, laying his hand on his shoulder, "are you hurt?"

James shook his head for he could not yet speak. "Aye," said the big man who held me, "he is a brave lad and no mistake."

We heard that the fire had been started by someone laying down a lighted pipe; I remember our John Manly's rule, never to allow a pipe in the stable.

30

We were taken to the house of my master's friend. We were well treated and after two or three days we returned home. We were glad to be in our own stable again, and John was equally glad to see us. Before he and James left us for the night, James said,

"I wonder who is coming in my place?"

"Little Joe Green, at the Lodge," said John.

"Little Joe Green! Why, he's only a child!"

"He's fourteen and a half," said John.

"But he is such a little chap. It will be hard for you to show him the work, John."

"Well," said John with a laugh, "work and I are very good friends. I never was afraid of work yet."

"You are a very good man," said James. "I hope a little of it has rubbed off on to me!"

31

Going for the Doctor

One night, a few days after James had left, I had eaten my hay and laid down in my straw fast asleep when I was suddenly woken by the stable bell ringing very loudly. I heard the door of John's house open and the sound of his feet running up to the Hall. He was back again in no time, he unlocked the stable door and came in, calling out,

"Wake up, Beauty, you must show now what you are made of," and almost at once he had got the saddle on my back and the bridle on my head. He ran round for his coat then rode me at a quick trot up to the Hall door. The Squire stood there with a lamp in his hand.

"Now John," he said, "ride for your life, that is for your mistress's life, there is not a moment to lose. Give this note to Dr White, give your horse a rest at the inn, and be back as soon as you can."

John said, "Yes, sir," and was on my back in a minute. Away we went, through the Park and through the village and down the hill, until we came to the toll-gate. John called very loudly and thumped on the door. The man was soon out, and flung open the gate.

"Now," said John, "you must keep the gate open for the doctor, here's the money," and off we went again.

There was (in front of us) a long piece of level road by the river. John said to me, "Now Beauty, do your best," and so I did. I needed no whip or spur, and for two miles I galloped as fast as I could lay my feet on the ground. When we came to the bridge John pulled me up a little and patted my neck.

"Well done, Beauty, good old fellow," he said. He would have let me go slower but my spirit was up and I was off again as fast as before. The air was frosty, the moon was bright, it was very pleasant. We came through a village, then through a dark wood, then uphill, then downhill, until after an eight mile run we came to the town, through the streets and into the Market Place. It was all quite still except for the clatter of my feet on the stones, for everybody was asleep. The church clock struck three as we drew up at Dr White's door. John rang the bell twice, and then knocked at the door like thunder.

A window was thrown up and Dr White in his night-cap, put his head out and said,

"What do you want?"

"Mrs Gordon is very ill, sir; master wants you to go at once, he thinks she will die if you cannot get there. Here is a note."

"Wait," he said, "I will come."

He shut the window and was soon at the door. "The worst of it is," he said, "that my horse has been out all day and is completely exhausted. My son has just been sent for and he has taken the other one. What shall we do? Can I have your horse?"

"He has come at a gallop nearly all the way, sir, and I was to give him a rest here, but I think my master would agree to your plan if he were here, sir."

"All right," he said, "I'll soon be ready."

I will not tell you about our way back. The doctor was a heavier man than John, and not so good a rider; however, I did my very best. The man at the toll-gate had it open, and soon we were in the Park. Joe was at the lodge gate, my master was at the hall door, for he had heard us coming. He spoke not a word. The doctor went into the house with him and Joe led me to the stable.

Joe Green

I was glad to get home, my legs shook under me, and I could only stand and pant. I had not a dry hair on my body, the water ran down my legs and I steamed all over. Poor Joe, he was young and small and he did the best he could. He rubbed my legs and chest but he did not put a warm blanket on me. Then he gave me a pail full of water to drink, it was cold and very good and I drank it all. Then he gave me some hay and some corn, and thinking he had done the right thing, he went away. Soon I began to shake and tremble and turned deadly cold, my legs ached, my chest ached. I felt cold and sore all over. Oh, how I wished for my warm thick blanket as I stood and trembled. I wished for John, but he had eight miles to walk, so I lay down in my straw and tried to go to sleep. After a while I heard John at the door. I gave a low moan for I was in great pain. He was at my side in a moment, stooping down by me. I could not tell him how I felt but he seemed to know it all. He covered me up with two or three warm cloths and then ran to the house for some hot water. He made me some warm gruel which I drank and then I think I went to sleep. John seemed to be very annoyed indeed. I heard him say to himself over and over again, ''Stupid boy! Stupid boy! No blanket put on and I expect the water was cold too. Boys are no good!''

I was now very ill; a strong inflammation had attacked my lungs and I could not draw breath without pain. John nursed me night and day. He would get up two or three times in the night to come to me, and the master would often come to see me too.

"My poor Beauty," he said one day. "My good horse, you saved your mistress's life, Beauty. Yes, you saved her life."

I was very glad to hear that, for it seems the doctor had said if we had been a little longer it would have been too late.

John told my master he had never seen a horse go so fast in his life. It seemed as if the horse knew what was the matter.

Of course I did, though John thought not. At least I knew as much as this, that John and I must go at top speed if we were to save the life of our mistress.

I do not know how long I was ill, but I judged from the odd word which I heard, that they thought I would die. Joe was broken-hearted about the matter for he had meant no harm, and John was quiet and sad. Finally, some medicine was sent which made me sleep deeply, and the next morning I felt very much better.

35

The Parting

For three years I lived at Birtwick, and they were three happy years, but sad changes were about to come upon us. We heard from time to time that our mistress was ill. The doctor was often at the house and the master looked grave and anxious. Then we heard that she had to leave her home immediately and go to a warm country for two or three years. Everybody was sorry, but the master began to make arrangements for breaking up the estate and leaving England. We used to hear it talked about in our stable, indeed nothing else was talked about.

The master arranged for Ginger and me to be sold to his old friend the Earl of Westerleigh, for he thought we would find a good home there. Merrylegs had been given to the Vicar, who was wanting a pony for Mrs Blomefield. This was on condition he was never sold and when he was past work he should be shot and buried. Joe was engaged to take care of him and to help in the house so I thought Merrylegs was well off. John had been offered several good jobs, but he decided to wait a little and look around. The master came to say his final farewell to John on the evening before his departure. They spoke little, and shook hands before parting.

The last sad day had come. The mistress was carried to the carriage and made comfortable. We trotted slowly through the Park and through the village where the people stood at their doors to have a last look, and to say God bless them. We reached the railway station and the mistress walked from the carriage to the waiting room. Joe stood by the horses while John went on to the platform. The train came in to the station, doors slammed, the guard whistled and the train glided away, leaving behind it only clouds of white smoke and some very heavy hearts.

When it was out of sight, John came back.

"We shall never see her again," he said, "never." He took the reins, mounted the box and with Joe rode slowly home, but it was not our home now.

Earlshall

The next morning after breakfast, Joe put Merrylegs into the mistress's low carriage to take him to the vicarage. He came first and said goodbye to us and Merrylegs neighed to us from the yard.

Then John put the saddle on Ginger and the leading rein on me, and rode us across the country about fifteen and a half miles to Earlshall Park, where the Earl of Westerleigh lived. There was a very fine house and many stables. We went into the yard through a stone gateway, and John asked for Mr York. It was some time before he came. He was very friendly and polite to John, and after giving us a glance, he called a groom to take us to our boxes. We were taken to a light airy stable, placed in boxes next to each other, rubbed down and fed. In about half an hour John and Mr York, who was to be our new coachman, came in to see us. He asked John to give his honest opinion of our performance and this John did. He mentioned Ginger's sad history and warned Mr York that she was liable to a little bad temper if she were not kindly handled. He also mentioned that we had not been used to a bearing rein.

"Well," said York, "if they come here, they must wear the bearing rein. I prefer a loose rein myself, and his lordship is always very

reasonable about the horses but my lady, that's another thing. She will have style and if her carriage horses are not reined up tight she wouldn't look at them. I always stand out against the gag-bit and shall do so, but it must be tight when my lady rides!''

"I am very sorry for it, very sorry," said John, "but I must go now, or I shall lose the train."

He came round to pat and speak to us for the last time, his voice sounded very sad. I held my face close to him, that was all I could do to say goodbye, and then he was gone, and I have never seen him since.

The next day Lord Westerleigh came to look at us, and he seemed pleased. York told him what John had said about us.

"Well," said he, "we must keep an eye on the mare, and put the bearing rein easy. I'll mention it to her ladyship."

In the afternoon we were harnessed, put in the carriage and taken round to the front of the house. The lady came down a flight of stone steps. She stepped round to look at us. She was a tall, proud-looking woman and seemed displeased about something, but said nothing and got into the carriage.

A Stand for Freedom

The next day we were again at the door. As she came down the steps I heard her ladyship say,

"York, you must put those horses heads higher, they are not fit to be seen."

York came round to our heads and shortened the rein himself, one hole I think. Then I began to understand what I had been told. Day by day, hole by hole, our bearing reins were shortened, and instead of looking forward with pleasure to having my harness put on as I used to do, I began to dread it. Ginger too seemed restless, though she said very little. One day the lady came down later than usual and seemed irritated.

"Are you never going to get those horses' heads up, York? Raise them at once."

He drew my head back and fixed the rein so tight that it was almost unbearable. Then he went to Ginger. She had a good idea of what was coming, and the moment York took the rein off in order to shorten it, she took her opportunity and reared up so suddenly that York had his nose roughly hit and his hat knocked off. The groom was nearly thrown off his legs. She went on plunging, rearing and kicking in a most desperate manner. At last, she kicked right over the carriage pole and fell down. York promptly sat himself down flat on her head to prevent her struggling, at the same time calling out orders to free me from Ginger and the carriage. I was led in to my box and later heard York muttering to himself,

"Confound these bearing reins, I thought we should have trouble soon."

Ginger was never put in to the carriage again but was given to one of the Lord's sons who was sure she would make a good hunter. As for me, I was obliged still to go in the carriage, and had a new partner called Max. He had always been used to the tight rein, but he hated it as much as I did.

The Lady Anne

Early in the spring, Lord Westerleigh and part of his family went to London and took York with them. Ginger and I and some other horses were left at home for use, and the head groom was left in charge. The Lady Harriet, who was an invalid, never went out in the carriage. The Lady Anne preferred riding on horseback with her brother or cousins. She was a perfect horse-woman and gentle as she was beautiful. She chose me for herself and named me Black Auster.
I enjoyed these rides very much in the clear cold air, sometimes with Ginger, sometimes with Lizzie. This Lizzie was a bay mare, a great favourite with the gentlemen because of her fine action and lively spirit. Ginger, who knew her better than I did, said she was rather nervous.

There was a gentleman of the name of Blantyre staying at the Hall. He always rode Lizzie and praised her so much that one day Lady Anne ordered the side saddle to be put on her, and the other saddle on me. When we came to the door, the gentleman seemed rather anxious.

"What's this?" he said. "Are you tired of your good Black Auster?"

"Oh no! not at all," she replied, "but I shall let you ride him for once, and I will try your charming Lizzie."

Blantyre pleaded with her to change her mind, saying that Lizzie was far too nervous for a lady to ride, but Lady Anne was determined and so we set out. We were riding to the house of Dr Ashley to deliver a note from the Lady Harriet. It was only a short journey and when we reached the gate, the Lady Anne said that she would wait with the horses while her cousin delivered the letter.

Blantyre hung my rein on one of the iron spikes and was soon hidden among the trees. My young mistress was sitting easily with a loose rein, humming a little song.

There was a meadow on the opposite side of the road, the gate of which stood open. Just then, some cart-horses and several young colts came trotting out in a very disorderly manner, whilst a boy behind was cracking a great whip. The colts were wild and frolicsome and one of them bolted across the road, and knocked up against one of Lizzie's hind legs. Whether it was the stupid colt, or the loud cracking of the whip or both together, I cannot say, but she gave a violent kick and dashed off into a headlong gallop. I gave a loud shrill neigh for help, pawed the ground impatiently, and tossed my head to get the rein loose. Blantyre came running to the gate, he looked anxiously about and just caught sight of the flying figure now far away on the road. He sprang into the saddle and seeing that I was as eager as he, he leaned a little forward and we dashed after them.

For about a mile and a half the road ran straight and then bent to the right, after which it divided into two roads. Which way had she turned? Mercifully, an old woman had seen her pass and cried out, ''To the right'', pointing with her hand. For a moment we caught sight of her, then another bend and she was hidden again. We came on to the common, which I knew well. The ground was rough and uneven, covered with heather and bushes; the worst place I ever knew for a headlong gallop. We were gaining on them now for the roughness of the ground had lessened Lizzie's speed. About halfway across the heath a wide dyke had been cut, and the earth from the cutting was piled roughly on the other side. Surely this would stop them! But no, with scarcely a pause Lizzie took the leap, stumbled on the loose earth and fell. Blantyre groaned, ''Now Auster, do your best!'' He gave me a steady rein, I gathered myself well together and with one determined leap, cleared both dyke and bank.

My poor young mistress lay motionless on the heather, her face to the earth. Blantyre kneeled down and called her name but there was no sound. Gently he turned her face upward, it was ghastly white and her eyes were closed. He got up and looked wildly around for help. Nearby two men were cutting turf. Blantyre's calling soon brought them to the spot and the foreman asked what he could do.

''Can you ride?''

''Well, sir, I'm not much of a horseman, but I'd risk my neck for the Lady Anne. She was kind and generous to my wife this past winter.''

''Then mount this horse, sir, you'll be quite safe, and ride to the doctor's and tell him to come immediately. Then go on to the Hall, tell them all that you know, and tell them to send a carriage with Lady Anne's maid.'' He somehow scrambled into the saddle, and with a ''Gee up,'' and a clap on my sides with both his legs, he started on his journey. I took him as best I could over the rough ground, and we made good speed on the high road. The news was taken in turn to the doctor and the Hall, and I was just turned into my box, although there was a great deal of hurry and excitement when word of the accident was passed round.

Ginger was saddled and sent off in great haste and I soon heard the carriage roll out of the yard.

Two days after the accident Blantyre paid me a visit. He patted and praised me very much and from the conversation I heard that my young mistress was now out of danger and would soon be able to ride again. This was good news to me, and I looked forward to a happy life.

Reuben Smith

When York went to London he left in charge of the stables a man named Reuben Smith. He was a gentle character, clever in his management of horses and could doctor them almost as well as a farrier, for he had lived with a veterinary surgeon for two years. He was a handsome man, a good scholar and had very pleasant manners. He had only one fault and that was his love of drink. He was not like some men, always at it; he used to keep steady for weeks or months together, but then he would break out and have a "bout" of it, as York would say, and be a disgrace to himself, a terror to his wife and a nuisance to everyone who came in contact with him. He had been dismissed from the Earl's service, but York spoke up for him, and Smith promised he would never touch another drop, so he was given another chance.

One day, early in April, I was brought out and harnessed to the light carriage. It was to be returned to the makers for overhauling, and as Colonel Blantyre was obliged to return to his regiment, it was arranged that Smith should drive him to town in it, and ride back, and for this purpose he took the saddle with him.

We left the carriage at the makers and Smith rode me to the White Lion and ordered the ostler to feed me well and have me ready for him at four o'clock. A nail in one of my front shoes had loosened as I came along and the ostler pointed this out to Smith.

"That will be all right until we get home," he answered roughly, for he was the worse for drink by the time he called for me. It was nearly nine o'clock when we finally left, and he galloped fast, giving me a sharp cut with his whip from time to time. The moon had not yet risen and it was very dark. The roads were stony, having been recently mended and going over them at that pace my shoe became looser. When we were near the turnpike gate, it came off. If Smith had been in his right senses he would have noticed something wrong in my pace; but he was too madly drunk to notice anything.

Beyond the turn-pike was a long piece of road on which fresh stones had been laid, large sharp stones over which no horse could be ridden quickly without risk of danger. Over this road, with one shoe gone, I was forced to gallop at my top speed, my rider meanwhile cutting into me with his whip, and cursing me because I did not go faster. Of course my shoeless foot suffered dreadfully. The hoof was broken and split down to the quick, and the inside was terribly cut by the sharpness of the stones.

This could not go on. No horse could keep his footing under such circumstances, the pain was too great. I stumbled, and fell with violence on both my knees. Smith was flung off by my fall, and owing to the speed I was going at, he must have fallen with great force. I soon recovered my feet and limped to the side of the road where it was free from stones. The moon had just risen above the hedge, and by its light I could see Smith lying a few yards beyond me. He did not move, but made one heavy groan. I could have groaned too, for I was suffering intense pain, both from my foot and knees, but horses are used to bearing their pain in silence. I made no sound but I stood there and listened. The road was very little used and at this time of night we might stay for hours before help came.

47

How it Ended

It must have been nearly midnight when I heard at a great distance the sound of a horse's feet. As the sound came nearer and nearer, I was almost sure I could distinguish Ginger's step. I neighed loudly and was overjoyed to hear an answering neigh from Ginger and men's voices.

They came slowly over the stones, and stopped at the dark figure that lay on the ground.

One of the men jumped out of the dog-cart and bent down over it. "It is Reuben," he said, "but he isn't moving." The other man followed and bent over him.

"He's dead," he said, "feel how cold his hands are." They raised him up but there was no life, and his hair was soaked with blood. They laid him down again and came and looked at me. They soon saw my cut knees. "Why, the horse has been down and thrown him! Who would have thought the black horse would have done that?"

Robert then attempted to lead me forward. I made a step but almost fell again. "Hello, he's bad in his foot as well as his knees. Look here! His hoof is all cut to pieces. I'm afraid it's the old trouble again. Reuben couldn't have been in his right senses to ride a horse over these stones without a shoe. Poor Susan, I'm afraid she suspected this when she came to my house. But what shall we do? There's the horse to get home as well as the body."

Then followed a conversation between them, until it was agreed that Robert as the groom should lead me, and that Ned must take the body. I shall never forget that night walk, it was more than three miles. Robert led me very slowly and I limped and hobbled on as best I could with great pain. I am sure he was sorry for me for he often patted and encouraged me, talking to me in a pleasant voice.

At last I reached my own box and had some corn, and after Robert had wrapped up my knees in wet cloths, he tied up my foot in a bran poultice to draw out the heat and cleanse it before the horse doctor saw it in the morning. I managed to get myself down on the straw and slept in spite of the pain.

The farrier examined my wounds the next day and said that he hoped the joint was not injured, and if so I should not be spoiled for work, but I would never lose the blemish.

As Smith's death had been so sudden and no one had been there to see it, there was an inquest held. Several people gave evidence of Smith's intoxicated state and I was cleared of all blame. His poor wife was heart-broken, and cursed the drink that had caused her husband's downfall.

49

As soon as my knees healed, I was turned into a small meadow for a month or two and though I enjoyed the freedom I felt rather lonely. I was delighted one day to see dear old Ginger come in through the gate, and I soon found out that it was not for our pleasure that she was brought to be with me. Her story was a sad one. She had been ruined by hard riding and was now turned out to see what rest would do. The Earl came to see us and seemed very annoyed.

"There is three hundred pounds thrown away for no earthly use," he said, "but what I mind most is that these horses of my old friend, who thought they would find a good home with me, are ruined. The mare shall have twelve months' run, and we'll see how she is then, but the black one must be sold. It's a great pity, but I could not have horses with knees like those in my stables."

Through the recommendation of York, I was bought by the master of the livery stables. I had to go by train which was new to me, but I took it quietly.

A Thief and a Rogue

I had always been driven by people who at least knew how to drive, but in this place I was to get my experience of all the different kinds of bad and ignorant driving to which we horses are subjected. I was a "job-horse", and was let out to all sorts of people who wished to hire me. As I was good-tempered and gentle, I think I was more often let out to the ignorant drivers because I could be depended upon. My time in this stable was not one I remember with any pleasure, though I hope I worked hard and did my best. Of course, there were good times as well as bad. I remember one morning I was put into a light carriage and taken to a house in Pulteney Street. Two gentlemen came out; the taller of them came round to my head, he looked at the bit and bridle and just shifted the collar with his hand to see if it fitted comfortably.

"Do you consider this horse wants a curb?" he asked.

"Well," said the man, "I should say he would go just as well without, he has a very good mouth, and though he has a fine spirit he has no temper. Generally though, we find people like the curb."

"I don't like it," said the gentleman. "Be so good as to take it off, and put the rein in at the check. An easy mouth is a great thing on a long journey, is it not, old fellow?" he said patting my neck.

Then he took the reins and they both got up. I can remember now how quietly he turned me round and then with a light feel of the rein and drawing the whip gently across my back, we were off!

I arched my neck and set off at my best pace. I found I had someone behind me who knew how a good horse ought to be driven. It seemed like old times again and made me feel quite light-hearted.

This gentleman took a great liking to me and after trying me several times with the saddle, he asked my master to sell me to a friend of his, who wanted a safe and pleasant horse for riding. And so it was that in the summer I was sold to Mr Barry.

My new master was unmarried. He lived in Bath and was a hard-working business man. His doctor advised him to take more exercise and so he bought me. He rented a stable a short distance from his lodgings and hired a man named Filcher as a groom. My master knew very little about horses but he treated me well, and I would have been content but for things he knew nothing of. He ordered the best hay with plenty of oats, crushed beans and bran, with vetches or rye grass as the man might think suitable. I heard the master order the food so I knew there was plenty and I thought I was well off.

For a few days all went well. My groom understood his business and I was kindly treated. He had been an ostler in one of the big hotels in Bath. He had given that up and now grew fruit and vegetables for the market. His wife bred and fattened poultry and rabbits for sale.

After a while it seemed to me that my oats were very short. I had the beans but bran was mixed with them instead of oats, and these were in very small amounts, not more than a quarter of what there should have been. In two or three weeks this began to tell upon my strength and spirits. I could not complain of course, but I was surprised that my master did not see that something was wrong. However, one afternoon he rode out into the country to see a friend of his, a gentleman farmer who lived on the road to Wells. This gentleman had a very quick eye for horses and after he had welcomed his friend, he said,

"It seems to me, Barry, that your horse does not look as well as he did when you first had him. Has he been well?"

"Yes, I believe so," said my master.

The other man began to feel me all over, and shook his head slowly.

"I can't say who eats your corn, my dear fellow, but I am sure it isn't your horse. I advise you to look into your stable a little more. I hate to be suspicious, but there are mean wretches wicked enough to rob a dumb beast of his food."

Dumb beast! Yes we are, but if I could have spoken I would have told my master where his oats went to. My groom used to come every morning about six o'clock and with him came a little boy who carried a covered basket. He used to go with his father into the harness room where the corn was kept and I could see them fill a little bag with oats out of the bin. Some days after this, just after the boy had left the stable, the door was pushed open and a policeman walked in, holding the child tightly by the arm, saying,

"Show me the place where your father keeps his rabbit foot."

Filcher was cleaning my feet at the time, but they soon saw him, and though he argued with them, they marched him off to the lock-up and his boy with him. I heard afterwards that the boy was freed from blame, but the man was sentenced to prison for two months.

In a few days my new groom came. He was a tall good-looking fellow, but if ever there was a villain in the shape of a groom, Alfred Smirk was the man. He attended to my basic needs but neglected to groom me thoroughly, and worst of all he left my stall filthy. It was not long before the stench and dampness affected my health and I had to be taken to the farrier for attention. With his treatment I soon recovered but Mr Barry was so disgusted at being deceived by his grooms that he decided to give up keeping a horse and to hire one when he needed to. I was therefore kept until my feet were quite sound and then I was sold again.

A Horse Fair

No doubt a horse fair is a very entertaining place to those who have nothing to lose, in any case there is plenty to see. Long strings of young horses out of the country, fresh from the marshes, and droves of shaggy little Welsh ponies, no higher than Merrylegs, and hundreds of cart-horses of all sorts with their long tails braided up and tied with scarlet cord. There were a good many horses like myself, handsome and high bred, but fallen into the middle class, through some accident or blemish, unsoundness of wind, or some other complaint. There were some splendid animals in their prime, and fit for anything, but round in the background there were a number of poor things, sadly broken down with hard work, with their knees buckling over and their hind legs swinging out at every step. There were some very dejected-looking old horses, with the under lip hanging down and the ears laying back heavily, as if there was no more pleasure in life, and no

more hope. There were some so thin that you could see their ribs and some with old sores on their backs and hips. These were sad sights for a horse to see, who does not know what the future may hold.

There was a great deal of bargaining, of running up and beating down, and, if a horse may speak his mind, I should say there were more lies told and more trickery at that horse fair than a clever man could describe. I was put with two or three other strong useful-looking horses, and many people came to look at us.

There was one man I took a liking to, and hoped he would come and buy me. He was not a gentleman but he spoke gently and from the way he handled me, I knew he was used to horses. His grey eyes were friendly and kind and he had a clean fresh smell about him, no smell of old beer and tobacco which I hated.

He offered twenty-three pounds for me but that was refused and he walked away. After him came a very hard-looking, loud-voiced man and I was afraid he would have me, but he walked off. Later the grey-eyed man returned. I could not help reaching out my head towards him. He stroked my face kindly.

"Well, old chap," he said, "I think we should suit each other. I'll give twenty-four for him."

"Say twenty-five and you shall have him."

"Twenty-four ten," said my friend in a very decided tone, "and not a penny more. Yes or no?"

"Done," said the salesman, "and you may depend upon it there's quality in that horse. If you want him for cab work, he's a bargain."

The money was paid on the spot and my new master took my halter, and led me out of the fair to an inn, where he had a saddle and bridle ready. He gave me a good feed of oats and stood by while I ate it. Half-an-hour later we were on our way to London, through pleasant lanes and country roads, until we came to the great London thoroughfare, on which we travelled steadily, until in the twilight we reached the great City. We passed through street after street. I thought we should never come to the end of them. We turned up one of the side streets and my owner pulled up at one of the houses and whistled. The door flew open and a young woman followed by a little girl and boy ran out. The children hugged their father as he dismounted.

"Now, then, Harry, my boy, open the gates and mother will bring us the lantern."

"Let me get him a bran mash while you rub him down," said the mother.

"Do Polly, it's just what he wants, and I know you've got a beautiful mash ready for me!"

A London Cab Horse

My new master's name was Jeremiah Barker but everyone called him Jerry. Polly, his wife, was a trim, tidy little woman, with smooth dark hair, brown eyes and a merry little mouth. The boy was nearly twelve years old, a tall frank good-tempered lad, and little Dorothy (Dolly they called her) was the image of her mother, at eight years old. They were all very fond of each other. I never knew such a happy contented family before or since.

Jerry had a cab of his own, and two horses which he drove and attended to himself. His other horse was a tall, white, rather large-boned animal called Captain. He was old now, but when he was young he must have been splendid. He still had a proud way of holding his head and arching his neck, in fact, he was a high-bred, fine mannered, noble old horse, every inch of him. He told me that in his early youth he went to the Crimean war. He belonged to an officer in the cavalry and used to lead the regiment.

57

The next morning, when I was well-groomed, Polly and Dolly came into the yard to see me and to make friends. Harry had been helping his father since the early morning. Polly brought me a slice of apple and Dolly a piece of bread and made as much fuss of me as if I had been the 'Black Beauty' of olden times. It was a great treat to be petted again, and talked to in a gentle voice, and I let them see as well as I could that I wished to be friendly. They decided to call me Jack after their last horse. Captain went out in the cab all morning, and in the afternoon I did the work. Jerry took great pains to fit the collar and bridle comfortably. There was no bearing rein, what a blessing that was! After driving through the side streets we came to a large cab stand where a number of cabs were drawn up waiting for passengers.

A broad-faced, jolly-looking man came up to us and looked me all over, and then, straightening himself up, with a grunt, he said,

"He's the right sort for you, Jerry. I don't care what you gave for him, he'll be worth it."

This man's name was Grant, but he was called Governor Grant. He had been on the stand longest and he took it upon himself to settle matters, or stop disputes.

He was generally a good-tempered, sensible man; but occasionally he took too much drink which made him bad-tempered.

The first week of my life as a cab-horse was very trying. I had never been used to London, and the noise, the hurry, the crowds of horses, carts and carriages that I had to make my way through, made me feel anxious. But I soon found out that I could trust my driver completely and then I relaxed a little and became used to it. Jerry was as good a driver as I had ever known, and what was better, he thought of his horse's comfort as well as his own. In a short time my master and I understood each other as well as a horse and man can do. Our stables, too, were pleasant and we were kept clean and well fed. He always gave us plenty of clean fresh water so that we could drink as we liked. On Sundays, we were allowed to rest. We worked so hard during the rest of the week, that I do not think we could have kept it up, but for that day.

Jerry Barker

I never knew a better man than my new master, he was kind and good and had principles as high as John Manly's. He was good-tempered and jovial, so that he had very few enemies. He liked making up little songs and singing them to himself. One he was very fond of was this:

Come, father and mother,
Come, sister and brother,
Come, all of you, turn to,
And help one another.

And so they did, for that entire family worked together and there was always plenty of laughter and fun between them.

Jerry hated time-wasters and it always made him angry if people wanted to go somewhere in a great hurry, simply because they hadn't organized their time properly. He always went at a good fair pace though, and would make an exception in a good cause. I remember well one morning, as we were on the stand waiting for a fare, that a young man carrying a heavy bag trod on a piece of orange peel and fell heavily. Jerry ran and lifted him up, and led him into a shop to sit down for a moment. After about ten minutes, the shopman called him back, and the young man said,

"Can you take me to the South-Eastern Railway? This fall has made me late, and it is vital that I catch the twelve o'clock train. I'll gladly pay you extra fare if you can get me there in time."

"I'll do my very best," said Jerry cheerfully, "if you think you are well enough, sir," for the man looked very pale and shaken.

"I must go," he said, "please, open the door and let's waste no more time."

The next minute, Jerry was on the box, with a word to me and a twitch of the rein which I understood. The streets were very full that day but we managed fairly well as far as Cheapside, where we came to a standstill for three or four minutes. The young man put his head out anxiously and said, "I think I shall never get there, if this goes on."

"I'll do all that can be done, sir," said Jerry. "I think we shall be in time. This hold-up cannot last much longer and your luggage is very heavy for you to carry, sir."

Just then, the cart in front of us began to move and things improved from then on. We whirled into the station, just as the great clock pointed at eight minutes to twelve o'clock.

"Thank God! We are in time," said the young man, "and thank you too, my friend, and your good horse, you have saved me more than I can tell you, take this extra half-crown."

"No, sir, no, thank you all the same. I'm glad we made it in time, but don't stay now, sir, the bell is ringing."

When Jerry returned to the rank he was teased for driving hard to earn a few extra shillings.

"Look here, mates," said Jerry. "The gentleman offered me an extra half-crown but I didn't take it. It was reward enough to see him catch his train."

"Well," said one, "you'll never be a rich man."

"Most likely not," said Jerry, "but I don't know that I shall be the less happy for that," and so saying he took his place at the rear of the line.

61

The Sunday Cab

One morning as Jerry had just put me into the shafts, a gentleman walked into the yard.

"Good morning, Mr Barker," said the gentleman. "I have come to make arrangements with you for taking Mrs Briggs regularly to church on Sunday mornings. We go to the new church now and it is rather further than she can walk."

"Thank you, sir," said Jerry, "but I only have a six days' licence and therefore I could not take a fare on a Sunday, it would not be legal."

"Oh," said the gentleman, "I did not realize yours was a six day licence, but it would be easy to alter it and I would make it worth your while."

"I should be glad to oblige the lady, sir, but I had a seven day licence once. The work was too hard for me and too hard for my horses. I like to spend Sunday with my wife and children and to go to church myself. I'm very sorry, sir."

"Oh, very well," said the gentleman. "Don't trouble yourself Mr Barker. I will make other inquiries," and he walked away.

It soon became known that Jerry had lost his best customer, and for what reason. Most of the men said he was a fool, but two or three agreed with him, and said it was every working man's right to rest on a Sunday.

Two or three weeks after this, as we came into the yard rather late in the evening, Polly came running across the road with a lantern.

"It has all worked out right, Jerry. Mrs Briggs sent her servant this afternoon to ask you to take her out tomorrow at eleven o'clock. Apparently, Mr Briggs was put out because you refused to come on Sundays and he has been trying other cabs, but there's something wrong with them all. The mistress says there is not one of them as nice and clean as yours and nothing will suit her but Mr Barker's cab again."

A Helping Hand

After this, Mrs Briggs wanted Jerry's cab as often as before, but never on a Sunday. But there came a day when we had Sunday work. Jerry was cleaning me in the yard when Polly came rushing out carrying a letter.

"Poor Dinah Brown has just heard that her mother is dangerously ill and that she must go to her immediately. The place is ten miles away and if she goes by train, there is still a four mile walk. She is still very frail and her baby is only four weeks old. She wants to know if you would take her in your cab; and she promises to pay you as soon as she can get the money," Polly said.

"Mmn, we'll see about that. It was not the money I was thinking about, but of losing our Sunday. The horses are tired and so am I," replied Jerry.

"I know," said Polly, "but we ought to treat others as we would like to be treated. I know how I'd feel in her place."

"You are right, my dear," said Jerry. "Go and tell Dinah I'll be ready for her at ten o'clock. Oh, and on the way back, go and see butcher Braydon and ask if he would lend me his light trap. He never uses it on a Sunday and it would make a great difference to the horse."

Away she went and soon returned, saying that he could have the trap and welcome. "All right now, just get me some bread and cheese packed up and I'll be back in the afternoon, as soon as I can."

It was a fine May day. When we were out of the town, the sweet air, the smell of the fresh grass and the soft country roads were as pleasant as they used to be in the old times, and I soon began to feel quite fresh.

Dinah's family lived in a small farm-house, up a green lane. There were two cows feeding near some shady trees. A young man asked Jerry to bring his trap into the meadow and he would tie me up in the cowshed. He wished he had a better stable to offer.

"If your cows would not be offended," said Jerry, "there is nothing my horse would like better than to have an hour or two in your beautiful meadow. He's quiet, and it would be a real treat for him."

"Do and welcome," said the young man. "You have been so kind to my sister. Perhaps you'll have some dinner with us, it will be ready in an hour or so." Jerry thanked him kindly, but said he had some dinner with him, and there was nothing he would like more than a stroll in the meadow.

When my harness was taken off, I did not know what I should do first, whether to eat the grass, or roll over on my back, or lie down and rest, or have a gallop across the meadow, and so I did each in turn. Jerry seemed to be just as happy as I was. He sat down by a bank, under a shady tree and listened to the birds. Then he sang to himself and read out of a little brown book he was so fond of. Then he wandered round the meadow and down by a little brook, where he picked some flowers and tied them up with long sprays of ivy. He gave me a good feed of oats which he had brought with him, and soon it was time to be on our way again.

We came home gently, and Jerry's first words were, as we came into the yard,

"Well, Polly, I have not lost my Sunday after all, for the birds were singing hymns in every bush and I joined in the service; and as for Jack, he was like a young colt." When he handed Dolly the flowers she jumped about for joy.

A Real Gentleman

The winter came early with a lot of cold and wet weather. There was snow or sleet or rain almost every day for weeks, sometimes with a keen wind or a sharp frost. The horses all felt it very much. When it is a dry cold, a couple of good thick rugs keep us warm, but when it rains, they get soaking wet and are no good. Some of the drivers were so poor that they felt the bad weather as much as the horses, having no warm or waterproof clothing. When it was very bad, many of them would go and sit in the tavern, but they often lost a customer in that way. Jerry preferred the coffee shop, or bought from an old man who came to the rank with hot coffee and pies. Polly always gave him something to eat when he could not get home, and sometimes little Dolly would come along with a plate of something hot. Jerry was drinking his soup one day, and Dolly was standing by him, when an elderly gentleman hailed

us. Jerry hurriedly returned the bowl to Dolly but the old man said,

"No, no, finish your soup, my friend. I can wait until you have finished and seen your little girl off safely." So saying, he seated himself in the cab. Jerry thanked him, and went on with his lunch.

"There Dolly, that's a gentleman, that's a real gentleman Dolly; he has got time and thought for the comfort of a poor cabman and his little girl."

Several times after that, the same gentleman took our cab. He was not young but he had a lively eye and a determined look about him. His voice was pleasant and kind, any horse would trust that voice. One

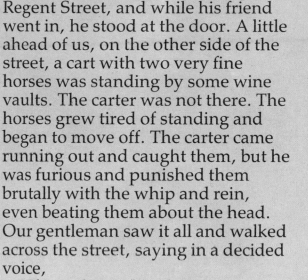

day, he and another gentleman took our cab. They stopped at a shop in Regent Street, and while his friend went in, he stood at the door. A little ahead of us, on the other side of the street, a cart with two very fine horses was standing by some wine vaults. The carter was not there. The horses grew tired of standing and began to move off. The carter came running out and caught them, but he was furious and punished them brutally with the whip and rein, even beating them about the head. Our gentleman saw it all and walked across the street, saying in a decided voice,

"If you don't stop that immediately, I'll have you summoned for leaving your horses, and for cruel conduct."

The man had obviously been drinking and he shouted some abuse as he got up into his cart. In the meantime, our friend had quietly been noting down the name and address painted on the cart.

On returning to our cab, our friend was joined by his companion who said laughingly, "I should have thought, Wright, that you had enough business of your own to look after, without bothering about other people's horses and servants."

Our friend threw back his head and answered,

"This world is as bad as it is because people only think about their own business. I never let a cruel act like this pass without doing what I can, and many a master has thanked me for letting it be known how his horses have been ill-treated."

"I wish there were more gentlemen like you, sir," said Jerry, "for they are wanted badly enough in this city."

Poor Ginger

One of the saddest days for me came some weeks later. Our cab, and several others, were waiting outside one of the parks where a band was playing. A scruffy old cab drove up drawn by an old worn-out chestnut horse, with an ill-kept coat and bones that showed plainly through it.

I had been eating some hay and the wind rolled a bit of it that way. The poor creature put out her long thin neck and picked it up, then turned round and looked for more. There was a hopeless look in the dull eye that I could not help noticing, and then as I was wondering where I had seen the horse before, she looked at me and said,

"Black Beauty, is that you?"

It was Ginger! But how she had changed. The beautifully arched and glossy neck was now straight and lank and fallen. The clean straight legs and delicate fetlocks were swollen; the joints were grown out of shape with hard work, the face that was once so full of spirit and life was now full of suffering and I could tell by the heaving of her sides and her frequent cough, how bad her breathing was.

Her story was a sad one and she could not bear to tell me all the details, only that she had been sold and sold again, each time getting lower, and falling into the hands of men who thought more of their money than their horse. She was a cab-horse now, working a full seven days a week with never a rest.

I said, "You used to stand up for yourself if you were badly treated."

"Ah," she said, "I did once, but it's no use, men are strongest and if they are cruel and have no feeling there is nothing that we can do, but just bear it, on and on to the end. I wish the end would come. I wish I was dead."

I was greatly upset, and I put my nose up to hers, but I could say nothing to comfort her. I think she was pleased to see me, for she said,

"You are the only friend I ever had."

Just then her driver came up and with a tug at her mouth, backed her out of the line and drove off leaving me very sad indeed.

A short time after this, a cart with a dead horse in it passed our cab-stand. The head hung out of the cart-tail, and I saw the sunken eyes. It was all too horrible to remember. It was a chestnut horse with a long thin neck. I saw a white streak down the forehead. I believe it was Ginger; I hoped it was, for then her troubles would be over. Oh! if men were more merciful they would shoot us before we came to such misery.

Jerry's New Year

Christmas and the New Year are very happy times for some people, but for cabmen and cabmen's horses, it is no holiday. There are so many parties, balls and places of amusement open, that the work is hard and often long. Sometimes driver and horse have to wait for hours in the rain or frost, shivering with cold, whilst the merry people inside are dancing away to the music. I wonder if the beautiful ladies ever think of the tired cabman waiting on his box and his patient horse standing until his legs get stiff with cold.

We had a great deal of late work in the Christmas week and Jerry's cough was bad, but however late we were, Polly waited up for him, and came out with the lantern to meet him, looking anxious and troubled.

On the evening of the New Year, we had to take two gentlemen to a house in the West End. We left them at nine o'clock and were told to come again at eleven. "But," said one of them, "as it is a card party, you may have to wait a few minutes, but don't be late." As the clock struck eleven we were at the door, for Jerry was always punctual. There was no sign of the gentlemen, so we waited. The weather had been changeable during the day and now it was very cold, with a sharp driving sleet. The hours passed and still no one came.

At half-past twelve Jerry rang the bell and asked the servant if he would be wanted that night.

"Oh yes, you'll be wanted all right," said the man. "You must not go, it will soon be over."

Again Jerry sat down, but his voice was so hoarse I could hardly hear him. At quarter past one, the men came out and got into the cab without a word. When they got out, they never apologised for keeping us waiting, but just complained because the fare was so high.

At last we got home. Jerry could hardly speak and his cough was dreadful. Polly asked no questions, but opened the door and held the lantern for him.

"Can I do something?" she said.
"Yes, get Jack something warm and then boil me some gruel."

This was said in a hoarse whisper; he could hardly get his breath, but he gave me a rub down as usual, and even went up into the hayloft for an extra bundle of straw for my bed. Polly brought me a warm mash that made me comfortable, and then they locked the door.

It was late the next morning before anyone came, and then it was only Harry. He cleaned us and fed us and swept out the stalls, but he looked solemn. In the afternoon he came again to give us food and water, and this time Dolly came with him. She was crying and I gathered from what they were saying that Jerry was dangerously ill and the doctor considered it to be a serious case of bronchitis. The Governor called several times and gave Harry a word or two of advice about caring for us. Jerry grew steadily better, but the doctor said he must never go back to cab work again. The children had many secret discussions together about what their mother and father would do, and how they could help earn money.

One afternoon, Harry was busy in the stable when Dolly came in.

"Who lives at Fairstowe, Harry? Mother has got a letter from Fairstowe. She seemed so pleased and ran upstairs to father with it."

"I believe that is where mother used to work, when she was maid to Mrs Fowler. Actually mother wrote to her last week. She always said she would help mother in any way she could, if anything happened to father."

Dolly went inside, but soon came back, dancing into the stable.

"Oh! Harry, you never heard such good news. We are to go to Fairstowe and live near Mrs Fowler. Her coachman is going away in the spring and father will do the work in his place. There's a cottage we can have, with a garden too, and a hen-house, and apple trees and everything!"

I never saw Jerry again. The children patted and stroked me and wished I could go with them, but it was not possible and I was sold again.

Hard Times

I was sold to a corn dealer and baker, whom Jerry knew and with him, he thought, I should have good food and fair work. I was not badly treated, but the work I was expected to do was heavy and the driver was free with his whip when he felt I was going too slowly. Good food and fair rest will keep up one's strength under reasonable work, but no horse can survive constant overloading. I was getting thoroughly pulled down, and in the end a younger horse was bought in my place, and I was sold to a large cab owner.

I shall never forget my new master. He had black eyes, a hooked nose; his mouth was as full of teeth as a bull-dog's and his voice was as harsh as the grinding of the cart wheels over gravel. His name was Nicholas Skinner. Skinner had a poor set of cabs and a poor set of drivers. He was hard on the men and the men were hard on the horses.

In this place we had no Sunday rest, and it was in the heat of the summer. My life became utterly wretched and I wished like Ginger just to die and be out of my misery, and one day my wish very nearly came true. We had taken a man to the railway station, and as a long train was expected, we pulled up at the back of the cabs there, and waited to see if we could get a return fare. A noisy, blustering man with his wife and two children engaged our cab and began to load their luggage on top. Box followed box until I felt the springs go down. The cab was loaded far too heavily and I could scarcely move it, but goaded by the constant chucks of the rein and the use of the whip, I did my best.

Suddenly, in a single moment, I cannot tell how, my feet slipped from under me and I fell heavily to the ground on my side. The force with which I fell seemed to beat all the breath out of my body. Someone said, "He's dead, he'll never get up again." I could hear a policeman giving orders, but I did not even open my eyes. Some cold water was thrown over my head and some medicine was poured into my mouth, and something was laid over me. I cannot tell how long I lay there, but I found my life coming back and a kind-voiced man was patting me and encouraging me to rise. After one or two attempts, I staggered to my feet and was gently led to some stables which were close by. In the evening, I was sufficiently recovered to be led back to Skinner's stables. The next morning, Skinner came with a farrier to look at me.

"This is a case of overwork more than disease. If you rest him and feed him up, he may pick up and you could get a few pounds for him I daresay."

Ten days of perfect rest, plenty of good oats, hay, bran mashes with boiled linseed mixed in them, did more to improve my condition than anything could have done.

When the twelfth day after the accident came, I was taken to a sale a few miles out of London. I felt that any change from my present place must be an improvement, so I held up my head and hoped for the best.

75

Farmer Thoroughgood

At this sale, of course, I found myself with some old broken-down horses, some so weak that I'm sure it would have been merciful to shoot them. Some of the buyers were hard, mean-looking men but there were others that I would have willingly used the last of my strength in serving. They were poor and shabby, but kind and human. Coming from the better part of the fair, I noticed a man who looked like a gentleman farmer, with a young boy by his side. He had a broad back and round shoulders, a kind ruddy face and he wore a broad-brimmed hat. He looked around and I saw his eyes rest on me.

"There's a horse, Willie, that has seen better days."

"Poor old fellow!" said the boy. "Do you think, grandpa, he was ever a carriage horse?"

"Oh yes, my boy," said the farmer coming closer, "look at his nostrils and his ears, the shape of the neck and shoulder. There's a good deal of breeding about that horse."

The boy pleaded with his grandfather to ask my price and the old gentleman laughed.

"We'll see," he said, feeling my legs and looking at my mouth.

"What is the lowest you will take for him?" he asked the dealer.

"Five pounds, sir, that was the lowest price my master set."

"Mmn. It's a gamble, but we'll try it. Could you lead him to the inn for me, please?"

They walked forward and I was led behind. The boy could hardly control his delight, and the old

gentleman seemed to enjoy his pleasure. I had a good feed at the inn, and was then gently ridden home by a servant of my new master and turned into a large meadow with a shed in one corner of it.

76

Mr Thoroughgood, for that was the farmer's name, gave orders that I should have hay and oats every night and morning and the run of the meadow during the day. The boy was to have charge of me, much to his joy. There was not a day when he did not pay me a visit, and give me a bit of carrot or something good.

He came with kind words and stroked me, and of course I grew very fond of him. The perfect rest, the good food, the soft turf and gentle exercise soon improved my condition and spirits. During the winter, my legs improved so much that I began to feel quite young again. One spring day, I was put before a light coach and Mr Thoroughgood and Willie drove me a few miles.

"He's growing young, Willie. We must give him a little gentle work now, and by midsummer I think he will be almost as good as new. I must be looking out for a quiet genteel place for him, where he will be well cared for and appreciated."

My Last Home

One day during this summer, the groom cleaned and dressed me with such extraordinary care that I thought some new change must be at hand. We drove a mile or two out of the village and came to a pretty, low house, with a lawn and shrubbery at the front and a drive up to the door. Willie rang the bell and asked for the mistress. Mr

Thoroughgood went into the house, while Willie stayed with me. He returned in about ten minutes, followed by three ladies, one tall pale lady, wrapped in a white shawl leaned on a younger lady, with dark eyes and a cheerful face, the other a very stately looking person was Miss Blomefield. They all came and looked at me and asked questions. It was finally agreed that I should stay for a short trial period and see how I made out. I was placed in a comfortable stable, fed and left to myself. The next day, when the groom was cleaning my face, he said,

"That is just like the star that Black Beauty had, he is much the same height too. I wonder where he is now?" He worked on and began to look me over carefully, talking to himself. "White star in the forehead, one white foot on the offside," then looking at the middle of my back, "and I'm darned if there isn't that little patch of white hair that John used to call 'Beauty's three-penny bit.' It must be Black Beauty! Why, Beauty! Beauty! do you know me? little Joe Green that almost killed you?" And he began patting and patting me as if he was quite overjoyed. I could not say that I remembered him, for he was grown up now, with black whiskers and a man's voice, but I was sure he knew me and that he was Joe Green, and I was very glad. I put my nose up to him and tried to say that we were friends. I never saw a man so pleased.

In the afternoon I was put into the low Park chair and brought to the door. The younger lady, Miss Ellen, was going to try me and Joe Green went with her. She seemed pleased with my paces and I heard Joe telling her about me and that he was sure I was Squire Gordon's old Black Beauty. When we returned, she told the other sisters what she had heard and said,

"I shall certainly write to Mrs Gordon and tell her that her favourite horse has come to us. She will be so pleased."

It was decided to keep me and call me by my old name of Black Beauty. I have now lived in this happy place a whole year. Joe is the best and kindest of grooms. My work is easy and pleasant and I feel my strength and spirits all coming back again. Mr Thoroughgood said to Joe the other day, "In your place he will last till he is twenty years old, perhaps more."

Willie always speaks to me when he can, and treats me as his special friend. My ladies have promised that I shall never be sold, and so I have nothing to fear; and here my story ends. My troubles are all over and I am at home; and often before I am quite awake, I fancy I am still in the orchard at Birtwick, standing with my friends under the apple tree.